Donald Crews
Parade

For all of you
I always remember
and for any of you
I sometimes forget

Greenwillow Books/New York

Copyright © 1983 by Donald Crews.
All rights reserved. No part of
this book may be reproduced or
utilized in any form or by any means,
electronic or mechanical, including
photocopying, recording or by any
information storage and retrieval
system, without permission in writing
from the Publishers, Greenwillow
Books, a division of William Morrow
& Company, Inc., 1350 Avenue of the
Americas, New York, NY 10019.
Printed in the United States of America
15 14 13 12 11 10 9 8 7 6 5 4

Library of Congress Cataloging in
Publication Data
Crews, Donald. Parade.
Summary: Illustrations and brief text
present the various elements of a
parade—the spectators, street vendors,
marchers, bands, floats, and the
cleanup afterwards.
1. Parades—Juvenile literature.
[1. Parades—Pictorial works] I. Title.
GT3980.C73 1983 394'.5 82-20927
ISBN 0-688-01995-1
ISBN 0-688-01996-X (lib. bdg.)

NO
PARADE
TODAY
PARKING

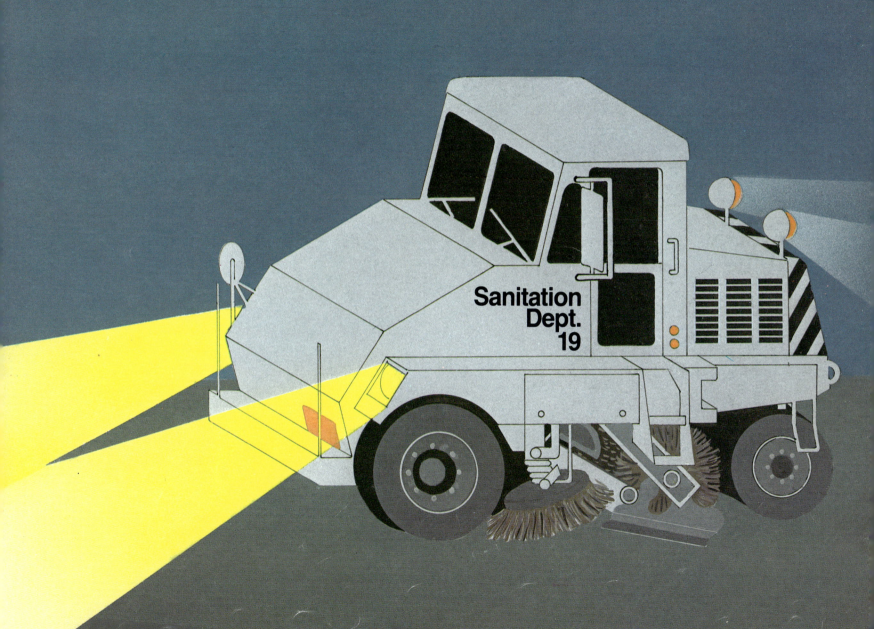

**Buttons,
balloons,
and flags
for sale.**

**Hot dogs,
pretzels,
ice cream,
and soda
to buy.**

ICE CREAM
CANDY
SODA

Watchers gather.

A crowd.   Waiting.

Flags
flying.

A strutting
drum major
leads the
marching band.

cornets,

trumpets, flutes,

French horns,   **sousaphones,**

field drums, cymbals, and last the big bass drums.

**Here comes
a float,**

and baton twirlers, twirling and turning.

Bicycles from bygone days,

and antique
automobiles,

a cruise ship,

and at the end
of the parade,
the brand-new
fire engine.

**Nothing left
to see,
nothing left
to do except . . .**